Santa needs a NEW BUM!

Dawn McMillan
Illustrated by
Ross Kinnaird

It's Christmas Eve day and I'm so excited.
I **LOVE** Christmas Eve nights!
I'm scrubbing carrots for the reindeer.
We're hanging up Christmas lights.

My heart is thumping.
My feet are jumping!

Because ...

Santa is coming our way.
He knows where we live.
He'll ride in on his sleigh.
He'll bring me a *mysterious* parcel
to open on Christmas Day.

Auntie and Pops
are making a **sign**.

Grandma's cooking
a **big** apple pie.

The cousins are **leaping**, **jumping** and **shrieking** as they laugh and point to the sky.

Santa!

He's early, and I'm wondering why …

Then with a **bump** and a **bang** …
a **clink** and a **clang** …

Santa has landed!
Right in front of me!

And now …

Amazing!
Incredible!

Who would believe it? **Santa** and I sit together for tea.

I'm listening.
I'm a good listener.
And I think Santa
has a **problem!**

Santa says, 'I should be happy at Christmas
but I'm not merry and bright.
My cheeks are rosy.
My whiskers are **white**.
The rest of me is feeling all right.
But ...'

I'm thinking … I'm thinking …
there must be a way
to save Santa's bum for Christmas Day.

It's **squeezed** and it's squashed. It's **WIDEWAYS** and **flat**.

Santa can't work
with a bum **shaped** like that.

'**Santa!**' I hear Big Sister shout.
'Leg lifts and lunges will help your bum out.'
But I'm thinking, no way.
Santa's too tired to do lunges today.

6

'Oh ... I forgot about the reindeer!'

'Oh let them come in,' Mum says with a **grin**.
'It's Christmas! No need to worry or fuss.

Nine reindeer! **How cool!**
They can come in and hang out with us.'

And **Santa** says, 'All this is fun
but I'm still **gloomy** and blue.
Because …

I desperately, **urgently**, absolutely …
need a bum that is new.'

My cousins are clever.

They're drawing new-bum designs.

But there's something *I've* been thinking about.

I know just what to do with a cushion or two.
Grandma will help me out.

We'll be making a gift for **Santa** to keep,
to thank him for being so kind.
For all the fun he brings with him
and the joy that he leaves behind.

The cushions ...

We sew and we **stuff** until they're **round** enough to make a new bum, Santa style.

It's **rosy** and **cosy**. **Snazzy** and **JAZZY**.

A bum to make **Santa** smile.

But where will we put it?
I'm looking ... I'm looking ...

And then ...

Santa is **staring**. His eyes start to *shine*.
'I see a present and I think it is mine!'

'Well I never! How very **clever**!
A **fantastic** new bum for me.
It's totally perfect for sitting,
and will SQUASH in a bit for chimney fitting.'

'I'm so **happy**, all thanks to you.
And now, my friends, I have work to do.
I have children to visit. Places to go.
Parcels to deliver, in fine weather or snow.'

With his new bum in place
and a **smile** on his face
Santa is ready to leave.

With a **big** present for me, and a wave for us all …

Santa's heading for Christmas Eve.

'Happy
Christmas,
everyone!'

About the author

Hi, I'm Dawn McMillan. I'm from Waiomu, a small coastal village on the western side of the Coromandel Peninsula in New Zealand. I live with my husband Derek and our cat, Joyce. I write some sensible stories and lots of funny stories! I love creating quirky characters and hope you enjoy reading about them.

About the illustrator

Hi. I'm Ross. I love to draw. When I'm not drawing, or being cross with my computer, I love most things involving the sea and nature. I also work from a little studio in my garden surrounded by birds and trees. I live in Auckland, New Zealand. I hope you like reading this book as much as I enjoyed illustrating it.

Published in the UK by Scholastic, 2024
1 London Bridge, London, SE1 9BG
Scholastic Ireland, 89E Lagan Road, Dublin Industrial Estate, Glasnevin, Dublin, D11 HP5F

SCHOLASTIC and associated logos are trademarks and/or registered trademarks of Scholastic Inc.

Originated in New Zealand by Oratia Media, 2024

Text © Dawn McMillan, 2024
Illustrations © Ross Kinnaird, 2024

The right of Dawn McMillan and Ross Kinnaird to be identified as the author and illustrator of this work has been asserted by them under the Copyright, Designs and Patents Act 1988.

ISBN 978 0702 33877 9

A CIP catalogue record for this book is available from the British Library.

Printed in the UK by Bell and Bain Ltd, Glasgow
Paper made from wood grown in sustainable forests and other controlled sources.

1 3 5 7 9 10 8 6 4 2

www.scholastic.co.uk

FSC
www.fsc.org
MIX
Paper | Supporting responsible forestry
FSC® C007785